W9-AZU-013

The Deep Sea

Matt Sims

High Noon Books
Novato, California

Cover and Interior Illustrations: Rick Hackney

International Standard Book Number: 1-57128-131-2

00 09 08 07 06 05 04 03
3 2 1 0 9

You'll enjoy all the High Noon Books. Write for
a free full list of titles.

Contents

The Rip Tide

Dave and Bill like to sail. They like to sail in the sea. Dave has a boat that has a big sail. The name of the boat is The Rip Tide.

Dave and Bill take The Rip Tide out to Gull

Rock every week. They
like to sail to Gull Rock.
On the way, they like to
see the seals.

Bill has a little boat.
It does not have a sail.
It has oars. Dave and
Bill use it as a life boat.

Dave and Bill tie the
little boat to the back of
The Rip Tide when they
go out to sea. They feel

*Dave and Bill tie the boat to the
back of The Rip Tide.*

safe when they have the little boat with them.

"See the waves?" said Bill.

"Yes, I see the waves," said Dave. "The waves are big. But this is a big boat. We will be safe."

The Seal

Dave and Bill set out for Gull Rock in The Rip Tide. They can hear the roar of the sea as the waves hit the side of the boat.

"What a nice day," said Dave.

"I like to sail when the sun is out, and it is nice and hot," said Bill.

"Look," said Dave. "I see a seal. I bet that seal is on its way to Gull Rock."

"We can race him," said Bill.

"If we race him, he will win," said Dave.

Then Dave and Bill

"Look," said Dave. "I see a seal."

saw the seal dive down deep in the sea.

"We will see more seals," said Bill. "There are a lot of seals out here."

The Log

"What is that?" said
Bill. "Is that the same
seal?"

"No," said Dave.
"That is not a seal.
That is a log."

"That log is in our
way," said Bill. "We will

hit it!"

Dave and Bill did not have time to get out of the way. The Rip Tide hit the log.

"Do you hear that hiss?" said Bill.

"Yes," said Dave. "I hear the hiss. And I can see a leak in the side of the boat."

The Rip Tide had hit

The Rip Tide hit the log.

the log. And there was a hole in the side of the boat.

"That is a big hole," said Dave. "The sea will fill this boat. Then the boat will go down!"

"We need to bail," said Bill.

"Get the pail and bail," said Dave. "I will fix the hole."

Save the Boat

"We can save this boat," said Dave.

Dave got a rag and put it in the save hole. Then he put tape over it.

"This will keep the sea out," said Dave.

"I hope it will," said

Bill. "That is a big hole, and that rag may pop out."

Then the tape gave way. Dave and Bill saw the rag pop out of the hole.

Dave and Bill could see the sea as it came in the boat.

"That hole is too big," said Dave. "We

"That hole is too big," said Dave.

can not fix it."

"And we can not keep the sea out with this pail," said Bill.

"The sea is up to my legs," said Dave. "This boat will go down! We have to get off this boat, or we will go down with it!"

The Little Boat

Dave and Bill got in the little boat. As they cut the rope, they saw The Rip Tide go down.

Now Dave and Bill had to make it to Gull Rock in the little boat.

"I will take the

*Now Dave and Bill had to make it
to Gull Rock in the little boat.*

oars," said Bill. "We are safe now. We will make it to Gull Rock."

With every wave that came, the little boat rose to its peak. Then it fell down the back side of the wave.

"Can you see Gull Rock?" said Bill.

"All I can see is the sea," said Dave.

Then a big wave hit the boat. Dave fell out of the boat. He fell in the sea.

"I will save you!" said Bill.

Bill got the rope. He had to toss the rope to Dave.

"I have it," said Dave.

Bill had to pull and

pull. But he got Dave to the side of the boat.

Dave got back in the boat. He was safe. But where was Gull Rock? Dave and Bill could not see it.

Gull Rock

"Look," said Dave. "I see sea gulls. They are from Gull Rock. Gull Rock has to be near. The sea gulls will lead us to it."

Then Bill said, "There it is. I see it!"

Over the peak of the waves, Dave could see Gull Rock.

Bill had to pull and pull on the oars, but he got the boat to the dock at Gull Rock. Dave tied the little boat up to the dock.

Dave and Bill were safe. They saw a pal and got a ride back from

Dave tied the little boat up to the dock.

him in his boat.

It had been a bad day out at sea. But Dave and Bill like the sea. Dave will get a new boat.

Will Dave and Bill take the little boat with them every time they sail?

You bet they will!

High Frequency Words

all	new	then
and	now	there
are	of	they
been	our	this
could	out	to
do	over	too
does	pull	was
down	put	what
every	said	when
from	saw	where
have	that	with
little	the	you
look	them	